PROJECT SUPER SOCKS

Master Plan

A place to keep all your sock-knitting blueprints

Christine Perry

Project Super Socks
Master Plan

Cover Design by Nicola Grossman

First edition published in the United Kingdom
November 2023 by Christine Perry

Publisher: Winwick Mum

ISBN-13: 978-1-9998919-2-3

Winwick
MUM

CONTENTS

Basic (plain) Socks

Cables

Lace

Colourwork

Other

Sock name

Sock name

Sock name

1

Made for ______________________________

Pattern

☐ cuff down ☐ toe up

Yarn

Needles

Cast on number	____ sts
Additional stitches	____ ankle ____calf ____foot ☐ none
No of rounds	____ cuff ____leg ____foot
Type of heel	☐ heel flap ☐ other ______________
Heel flap	______sts ______ rows No of V sts ____
Type of toe	
Leg length	
Foot length	Shoe size ______
Heel flap length	
Total foot length	

Decrease to _____ sts for toes ______ sts each side

Weight of sock	One sock ____ g/oz Two socks ____ g/oz
Amount of yarn used	Started with ____ g/oz Finished with ____ g/oz
Additional notes	
Date started	
Date finished	
Not finished? ☐	Why not?

Sock name

2

Made for ________________________________

Pattern

☐ cuff down ☐ toe up

Yarn

Needles

Cast on number	____ sts
Additional stitches	____ ankle ____calf ____foot ☐ none
No of rounds	____ cuff ____leg ____foot
Type of heel	☐ heel flap ☐ other ______________
Heel flap	______sts ______ rows No of V sts ____
Type of toe	
Leg length	
Foot length	Shoe size _______
Heel flap length	
Total foot length	

Decrease to _____ sts for toes _______ sts each side

Weight of sock	One sock ____ g/oz Two socks ___ g/oz
Amount of yarn used	Started with ____ g/oz Finished with ____ g/oz

Additional notes

Date started	
Date finished	
Not finished? ☐	Why not?

Sock name

3

Made for ______________________________

Pattern

☐ cuff down ☐ toe up

Yarn

Needles

Cast on number	____ sts
Additional stitches	____ ankle ____calf ____foot ☐ none
No of rounds	____ cuff ____leg ____foot
Type of heel	☐ heel flap ☐ other ____________
Heel flap	______sts ______ rows No of V sts ____
Type of toe	
Leg length	
Foot length	Shoe size ______
Heel flap length	
Total foot length	

Decrease to _____ sts for toes ______ sts each side

Weight of sock	One sock ____ g/oz Two socks ___ g/oz
Amount of yarn used	Started with ____ g/oz Finished with ____ g/oz
Additional notes	
Date started	
Date finished	
Not finished? ☐	Why not?

Sock name

4

Made for ______________________________

Pattern

☐ cuff down ☐ toe up

Yarn

Needles

Cast on number	____ sts
Additional stitches	____ ankle ____calf ____foot ☐ none
No of rounds	____ cuff ____leg ____foot
Type of heel	☐ heel flap ☐ other ______________
Heel flap	______sts ______ rows No of V sts ____
Type of toe	
Leg length	
Foot length	Shoe size _______
Heel flap length	
Total foot length	

Decrease to _____ sts for toes ______ sts each side

Weight of sock	One sock ____ g/oz Two socks ___ g/oz
Amount of yarn used	Started with ____ g/oz Finished with ____ g/oz

Additional notes

Date started	
Date finished	
Not finished? ☐	Why not?

Sock name

5

Made for ________________________________

Pattern

☐ cuff down ☐ toe up

Yarn

Needles

Cast on number	____ sts
Additional stitches	____ ankle ____calf ____foot ☐ none
No of rounds	____ cuff ____leg ____foot
Type of heel	☐ heel flap ☐ other ________________
Heel flap	______sts ______ rows No of V sts ____
Type of toe	
Leg length	
Foot length	Shoe size _______
Heel flap length	
Total foot length	

Decrease to _____ sts for toes _______ sts each side

Weight of sock	One sock ____ g/oz Two socks ___ g/oz
Amount of yarn used	Started with ____ g/oz Finished with ____ g/oz
Additional notes	
Date started	
Date finished	
Not finished? ☐	Why not?

Sock name 6

Made for ______________________________

Pattern

☐ cuff down ☐ toe up

Yarn

Needles

Cast on number	____ sts
Additional stitches	____ ankle ____calf ____foot ☐ none
No of rounds	____ cuff ____leg ____foot
Type of heel	☐ heel flap ☐ other ______________
Heel flap	______sts ______ rows No of V sts ____
Type of toe	
Leg length	
Foot length	Shoe size ______
Heel flap length	
Total foot length	

Decrease to _____ sts for toes ______ sts each side

Weight of sock	One sock ____ g/oz Two socks ____ g/oz
Amount of yarn used	Started with ____ g/oz Finished with ____ g/oz
Additional notes	
Date started	
Date finished	
Not finished? ☐	Why not?

Sock name

Made for ______________________________

Pattern

☐ cuff down ☐ toe up

Yarn

Needles

Cast on number	____ sts
Additional stitches	____ ankle ____calf ____foot ☐ none
No of rounds	____ cuff ____leg ____foot
Type of heel	☐ heel flap ☐ other ____________
Heel flap	______sts ______ rows No of V sts ____
Type of toe	
Leg length	
Foot length	Shoe size _______
Heel flap length	
Total foot length	

Decrease to _____ sts for toes ______ sts each side

Weight of sock	One sock ____ g/oz Two socks ___ g/oz
Amount of yarn used	Started with ____ g/oz Finished with ____ g/oz

Additional notes

Date started	
Date finished	
Not finished? ☐	Why not?

Sock name 8

Made for ______________________________

Pattern

☐ cuff down ☐ toe up

Yarn

Needles

Cast on number	____ sts
Additional stitches	____ ankle ____calf ____foot ☐ none
No of rounds	____ cuff ____leg ____foot
Type of heel	☐ heel flap ☐ other ______________
Heel flap	_____sts _____ rows No of V sts ____
Type of toe	
Leg length	
Foot length	Shoe size ______
Heel flap length	
Total foot length	

Decrease to _____ sts for toes ______ sts each side

Weight of sock	One sock ____ g/oz Two socks ___ g/oz
Amount of yarn used	Started with ____ g/oz Finished with ____ g/oz
Additional notes	
Date started	
Date finished	
Not finished? ☐	Why not?

Sock name

Made for ____________________________

Pattern

☐ cuff down ☐ toe up

Yarn

Needles

Cast on number	____ sts
Additional stitches	____ ankle ____calf ____foot ☐ none
No of rounds	____ cuff ____leg ____foot
Type of heel	☐ heel flap ☐ other ____________
Heel flap	______sts ______ rows No of V sts ____
Type of toe	
Leg length	
Foot length	Shoe size ________
Heel flap length	
Total foot length	

Decrease to _____ sts for toes ______ sts each side

Weight of sock	One sock ____ g/oz Two socks ___ g/oz
Amount of yarn used	Started with ____ g/oz Finished with ____ g/oz
Additional notes	
Date started	
Date finished	
Not finished? ☐	Why not?

Sock name

Made for ______________________________

Pattern

☐ cuff down ☐ toe up

Yarn

Needles

Cast on number	____ sts
Additional stitches	____ ankle ____calf ____foot ☐ none
No of rounds	____ cuff ____leg ____foot
Type of heel	☐ heel flap ☐ other ________________
Heel flap	______sts ______ rows No of V sts ____
Type of toe	
Leg length	
Foot length	Shoe size _______
Heel flap length	
Total foot length	

Decrease to _____ sts for toes ______ sts each side

Weight of sock	One sock ____ g/oz Two socks ___ g/oz
Amount of yarn used	Started with ____ g/oz Finished with ____ g/oz
Additional notes	
Date started	
Date finished	
Not finished? ☐	Why not?

Sock name

Made for ______________________________

Pattern

☐ cuff down ☐ toe up

Yarn

Needles

Cast on number	____ sts
Additional stitches	____ ankle ____calf ____foot ☐ none
No of rounds	____ cuff ____leg ____foot
Type of heel	☐ heel flap ☐ other ________________
Heel flap	______sts ______ rows No of V sts ____
Type of toe	
Leg length	
Foot length	Shoe size _______
Heel flap length	
Total foot length	

Decrease to _____ sts for toes _______ sts each side

Weight of sock	One sock ____ g/oz Two socks ___ g/oz
Amount of yarn used	Started with ____ g/oz Finished with ____ g/oz

Additional notes

Date started	
Date finished	

Not finished? ☐ Why not?

Sock name

12 

Made for ______________________________

Pattern

☐ cuff down ☐ toe up

Yarn

Needles

Cast on number	____ sts
Additional stitches	____ ankle ____calf ____foot ☐ none
No of rounds	____ cuff ____leg ____foot
Type of heel	☐ heel flap ☐ other ______________
Heel flap	_____sts _____ rows No of V sts ____
Type of toe	
Leg length	
Foot length	Shoe size ______
Heel flap length	
Total foot length	

Decrease to _____ sts for toes ______ sts each side

Weight of sock	One sock ____ g/oz Two socks ___ g/oz
Amount of yarn used	Started with ____ g/oz Finished with ____ g/oz
Additional notes	
Date started	
Date finished	
Not finished? ☐	Why not?

Sock name

Made for ______________________________

Pattern

☐ cuff down ☐ toe up

Yarn

Needles

Cast on number	____ sts
Additional stitches	____ ankle ____calf ____foot ☐ none
No of rounds	____ cuff ____leg ____foot
Type of heel	☐ heel flap ☐ other ______________
Heel flap	______sts ______ rows No of V sts ____
Type of toe	
Leg length	
Foot length	Shoe size ______
Heel flap length	
Total foot length	

Decrease to _____ sts for toes ______ sts each side

Weight of sock	One sock ____ g/oz Two socks ____ g/oz
Amount of yarn used	Started with ____ g/oz Finished with ____ g/oz

Additional notes

Date started	
Date finished	
Not finished? ☐	Why not?

Sock name

14

Made for ______________________________

Pattern

☐ cuff down ☐ toe up

Yarn

Needles

Cast on number	____ sts
Additional stitches	____ ankle ____calf ____foot ☐ none
No of rounds	____ cuff ____leg ____foot
Type of heel	☐ heel flap ☐ other ______________
Heel flap	______sts ______ rows No of V sts ____
Type of toe	
Leg length	
Foot length	Shoe size ______
Heel flap length	
Total foot length	

Decrease to _____ sts for toes ______ sts each side

Weight of sock	One sock ____ g/oz Two socks ___ g/oz
Amount of yarn used	Started with ____ g/oz Finished with ____ g/oz
Additional notes	
Date started	
Date finished	
Not finished? ☐	Why not?

Sock name

15

Made for ______________________________

Pattern

☐ cuff down ☐ toe up

Yarn

Needles

Cast on number	____ sts
Additional stitches	____ ankle ____calf ____foot ☐ none
No of rounds	____ cuff ____leg ____foot
Type of heel	☐ heel flap ☐ other ______________
Heel flap	______sts ______ rows No of V sts ____
Type of toe	
Leg length	
Foot length	Shoe size _______
Heel flap length	
Total foot length	

Decrease to ______ sts for toes _______ sts each side

Weight of sock	One sock ____ g/oz Two socks ___ g/oz
Amount of yarn used	Started with ____ g/oz Finished with ____ g/oz

Additional notes

Date started	
Date finished	
Not finished? ☐	Why not?

Sock name 16

Made for ______________________________

Pattern

☐ cuff down ☐ toe up

Yarn

Needles

Cast on number	____ sts
Additional stitches	____ ankle ____calf ____foot ☐ none
No of rounds	____ cuff ____leg ____foot
Type of heel	☐ heel flap ☐ other ______________
Heel flap	______sts ______ rows No of V sts ____
Type of toe	
Leg length	
Foot length	Shoe size ______
Heel flap length	
Total foot length	

Decrease to _____ sts for toes ______ sts each side

Weight of sock	One sock ____ g/oz Two socks ____ g/oz
Amount of yarn used	Started with ____ g/oz Finished with ____ g/oz

Additional notes

Date started	
Date finished	
Not finished? ☐	Why not?

Sock name

Made for ________________________________

Pattern

☐ cuff down ☐ toe up

Yarn

Needles

Cast on number	____ sts
Additional stitches	____ ankle ____calf ____foot ☐ none
No of rounds	____ cuff ____leg ____foot
Type of heel	☐ heel flap ☐ other ______________
Heel flap	______sts ______ rows No of V sts ____
Type of toe	
Leg length	
Foot length	Shoe size ______
Heel flap length	
Total foot length	

Decrease to _____ sts for toes ______ sts each side

Weight of sock	One sock ____ g/oz Two socks ___ g/oz
Amount of yarn used	Started with ____ g/oz Finished with ____ g/oz

Additional notes

Date started	
Date finished	
Not finished? ☐	Why not?

Sock name

Made for ______________________________

Pattern

☐ cuff down ☐ toe up

Yarn

Needles

Cast on number	____ sts
Additional stitches	____ ankle ____calf ____foot ☐ none
No of rounds	____ cuff ____leg ____foot
Type of heel	☐ heel flap ☐ other ______________
Heel flap	_____sts _____ rows No of V sts ____
Type of toe	
Leg length	
Foot length	Shoe size ______
Heel flap length	
Total foot length	

Decrease to _____ sts for toes _____ sts each side

Weight of sock	One sock ____ g/oz Two socks ___ g/oz
Amount of yarn used	Started with ____ g/oz Finished with ____ g/oz
Additional notes	
Date started	
Date finished	
Not finished? ☐	Why not?

Sock name

Made for ______________________________

Pattern

☐ cuff down ☐ toe up

Yarn

Needles

Cast on number	____ sts
Additional stitches	____ ankle ____calf ____foot ☐ none
No of rounds	____ cuff ____leg ____foot
Type of heel	☐ heel flap ☐ other ________________
Heel flap	______sts ______ rows No of V sts ____
Type of toe	
Leg length	
Foot length	Shoe size _______
Heel flap length	
Total foot length	

Decrease to _____ sts for toes _______ sts each side

Weight of sock	One sock ____ g/oz Two socks ___ g/oz
Amount of yarn used	Started with ____ g/oz Finished with ____ g/oz

Additional notes	
Date started	
Date finished	
Not finished? ☐	Why not?

Sock name

Made for ______________________________

Pattern

☐ cuff down ☐ toe up

Yarn

Needles

Cast on number	____ sts
Additional stitches	____ ankle ____calf ____foot ☐ none
No of rounds	____ cuff ____leg ____foot
Type of heel	☐ heel flap ☐ other ________________
Heel flap	______sts ______ rows No of V sts ____
Type of toe	
Leg length	
Foot length	Shoe size _______
Heel flap length	
Total foot length	

Decrease to _____ sts for toes _______ sts each side

Weight of sock	One sock ____ g/oz Two socks ___ g/oz
Amount of yarn used	Started with ____ g/oz Finished with ____ g/oz

Additional notes

Date started	
Date finished	

Not finished? ☐ Why not?

Sock name

21

Made for ______________________________

Pattern

☐ cuff down ☐ toe up

Yarn

Needles

Cast on number	____ sts
Additional stitches	____ ankle ____calf ____foot ☐ none
No of rounds	____ cuff ____leg ____foot
Type of heel	☐ heel flap ☐ other ______________
Heel flap	______sts ______ rows No of V sts ____
Type of toe	
Leg length	
Foot length	Shoe size _______
Heel flap length	
Total foot length	

Decrease to _____ sts for toes ______ sts each side

Weight of sock	One sock ____ g/oz Two socks ___ g/oz
Amount of yarn used	Started with ____ g/oz Finished with ____ g/oz

Additional notes

Date started	
Date finished	

Not finished? ☐	Why not?

Sock name

22 

Made for ______________________________

Pattern

☐ cuff down ☐ toe up

Yarn

Needles

Cast on number	____ sts
Additional stitches	____ ankle ____calf ____foot ☐ none
No of rounds	____ cuff ____leg ____foot
Type of heel	☐ heel flap ☐ other ______________
Heel flap	______sts ______ rows No of V sts ____
Type of toe	
Leg length	
Foot length	Shoe size _______
Heel flap length	
Total foot length	

Decrease to _____ sts for toes ______ sts each side

Weight of sock	One sock ____ g/oz Two socks ___ g/oz
Amount of yarn used	Started with ____ g/oz Finished with ____ g/oz
Additional notes	
Date started	
Date finished	
Not finished? ☐	Why not?

Sock name

23

Made for ______________________________

Pattern	
	☐ cuff down ☐ toe up
Yarn	
Needles	
Cast on number	____ sts
Additional stitches	____ ankle ____calf ____foot ☐ none
No of rounds	____ cuff ____leg ____foot
Type of heel	☐ heel flap ☐ other ________________
Heel flap	______sts ______ rows No of V sts ____
Type of toe	
Leg length	
Foot length	Shoe size _______
Heel flap length	
Total foot length	

Decrease to _____ sts for toes ______ sts each side

Weight of sock	One sock ____ g/oz Two socks ___ g/oz
Amount of yarn used	Started with ____ g/oz Finished with ____ g/oz
Additional notes	
Date started	
Date finished	
Not finished? ☐	Why not?

Sock name

24

Made for ______________________________

Pattern

☐ cuff down ☐ toe up

Yarn

Needles

Cast on number	____ sts
Additional stitches	____ ankle ____calf ____foot ☐ none
No of rounds	____ cuff ____leg ____foot
Type of heel	☐ heel flap ☐ other ______________
Heel flap	______sts ______ rows No of V sts ____
Type of toe	
Leg length	
Foot length	Shoe size _______
Heel flap length	
Total foot length	

Decrease to _____ sts for toes _______ sts each side

Weight of sock	One sock ____ g/oz Two socks ___ g/oz
Amount of yarn used	Started with ____ g/oz Finished with ____ g/oz

Additional notes

Date started	
Date finished	
Not finished? ☐	Why not?

Sock name

25 

Made for ______________________________

Pattern

☐ cuff down ☐ toe up

Yarn

Needles

Cast on number	____ sts
Additional stitches	____ ankle ____calf ____foot ☐ none
No of rounds	____ cuff ____leg ____foot
Type of heel	☐ heel flap ☐ other ________________
Heel flap	______sts ______ rows No of V sts ____
Type of toe	
Leg length	
Foot length	Shoe size _______
Heel flap length	
Total foot length	

Decrease to _____ sts for toes _______ sts each side

Weight of sock	One sock ____ g/oz Two socks ___ g/oz
Amount of yarn used	Started with ____ g/oz Finished with ____ g/oz

Additional notes

Date started	
Date finished	
Not finished? ☐	Why not?

Sock name

26

Made for ______________________________

Pattern

☐ cuff down ☐ toe up

Yarn

Needles

Cast on number	____ sts
Additional stitches	____ ankle ____calf ____foot ☐ none
No of rounds	____ cuff ____leg ____foot
Type of heel	☐ heel flap ☐ other ______________
Heel flap	______sts ______ rows No of V sts ____
Type of toe	
Leg length	
Foot length	Shoe size _______
Heel flap length	
Total foot length	

Decrease to _____ sts for toes _______ sts each side

Weight of sock	One sock ____ g/oz Two socks ___ g/oz
Amount of yarn used	Started with ____ g/oz Finished with ____ g/oz
Additional notes	
Date started	
Date finished	
Not finished? ☐	Why not?

Sock name 27 

Made for ______________________________

Pattern

☐ cuff down ☐ toe up

Yarn

Needles

Cast on number	____ sts
Additional stitches	____ ankle ____calf ____foot ☐ none
No of rounds	____ cuff ____leg ____foot
Type of heel	☐ heel flap ☐ other ________________
Heel flap	______sts ______ rows No of V sts ____
Type of toe	
Leg length	
Foot length	Shoe size _______
Heel flap length	
Total foot length	

Decrease to _____ sts for toes _______ sts each side

Weight of sock	One sock ____ g/oz Two socks ___ g/oz
Amount of yarn used	Started with ____ g/oz Finished with ____ g/oz
Additional notes	
Date started	
Date finished	
Not finished? ☐	Why not?

Sock name

28

Made for ______________________________

Pattern

☐ cuff down ☐ toe up

Yarn

Needles

Cast on number	____ sts
Additional stitches	____ ankle ____calf ____foot ☐ none
No of rounds	____ cuff ____leg ____foot
Type of heel	☐ heel flap ☐ other _______________
Heel flap	______sts ______ rows No of V sts ____
Type of toe	
Leg length	
Foot length	Shoe size _______
Heel flap length	
Total foot length	

Decrease to _____ sts for toes _______ sts each side

Weight of sock	One sock ____ g/oz Two socks ___ g/oz
Amount of yarn used	Started with ____ g/oz Finished with ____ g/oz

Additional notes

Date started	
Date finished	
Not finished? ☐	Why not?

Sock name

Made for ______________________________

Pattern

☐ cuff down ☐ toe up

Yarn

Needles

Cast on number	____ sts
Additional stitches	____ ankle ____calf ____foot ☐ none
No of rounds	____ cuff ____leg ____foot
Type of heel	☐ heel flap ☐ other _____________
Heel flap	______sts ______ rows No of V sts ____
Type of toe	
Leg length	
Foot length	Shoe size _______
Heel flap length	
Total foot length	

Decrease to _____ sts for toes ______ sts each side

Weight of sock	One sock ____ g/oz Two socks ____ g/oz
Amount of yarn used	Started with ____ g/oz Finished with ____ g/oz
Additional notes	
Date started	
Date finished	
Not finished? ☐	Why not?

Sock name

Made for ______________________________

Pattern

☐ cuff down ☐ toe up

Yarn

Needles

Cast on number	____ sts
Additional stitches	____ ankle ____calf ____foot ☐ none
No of rounds	____ cuff ____leg ____foot
Type of heel	☐ heel flap ☐ other ______________
Heel flap	______sts ______ rows No of V sts ____
Type of toe	
Leg length	
Foot length	Shoe size _______
Heel flap length	
Total foot length	

Decrease to _____ sts for toes _______ sts each side

Weight of sock	One sock ____ g/oz Two socks ___ g/oz
Amount of yarn used	Started with ____ g/oz Finished with ____ g/oz
Additional notes	
Date started	
Date finished	
Not finished? ☐	Why not?

Sock name

Made for ______________________________

Pattern

☐ cuff down ☐ toe up

Yarn

Needles

Cast on number	____ sts
Additional stitches	____ ankle ____calf ____foot ☐ none
No of rounds	____ cuff ____leg ____foot
Type of heel	☐ heel flap ☐ other ______________
Heel flap	______sts ______ rows No of V sts ____
Type of toe	
Leg length	
Foot length	Shoe size ______
Heel flap length	
Total foot length	

Decrease to _____ sts for toes ______ sts each side

Weight of sock	One sock ____ g/oz Two socks ___ g/oz
Amount of yarn used	Started with ____ g/oz Finished with ____ g/oz
Additional notes	
Date started	
Date finished	
Not finished? ☐	Why not?

Sock name

32

Made for ______________________________

Pattern

☐ cuff down ☐ toe up

Yarn

Needles

Cast on number	____ sts
Additional stitches	____ ankle ____calf ____foot ☐ none
No of rounds	____ cuff ____leg ____foot
Type of heel	☐ heel flap ☐ other ______________
Heel flap	_____sts _____ rows No of V sts ____
Type of toe	
Leg length	
Foot length	Shoe size ______
Heel flap length	
Total foot length	

Decrease to _____ sts for toes ______ sts each side

Weight of sock	One sock ____ g/oz Two socks ___ g/oz
Amount of yarn used	Started with ____ g/oz Finished with ____ g/oz

Additional notes

Date started	
Date finished	

Not finished? ☐ Why not?

Sock name

Made for ______________________________

Pattern

☐ cuff down ☐ toe up

Yarn

Needles

Cast on number	____ sts
Additional stitches	____ ankle ____calf ____foot ☐ none
No of rounds	____ cuff ____leg ____foot
Type of heel	☐ heel flap ☐ other ________________
Heel flap	______sts ______ rows No of V sts ____
Type of toe	
Leg length	
Foot length	Shoe size _______
Heel flap length	
Total foot length	

Decrease to _____ sts for toes ______ sts each side

Weight of sock	One sock ____ g/oz Two socks ___ g/oz
Amount of yarn used	Started with ____ g/oz Finished with ____ g/oz
Additional notes	
Date started	
Date finished	
Not finished? ☐	Why not?

Sock name 34

Made for ______________________________

Pattern

☐ cuff down ☐ toe up

Yarn

Needles

Cast on number	____ sts
Additional stitches	____ ankle ____calf ____foot ☐ none
No of rounds	____ cuff ____leg ____foot
Type of heel	☐ heel flap ☐ other ______________
Heel flap	______sts ______ rows No of V sts ____
Type of toe	
Leg length	
Foot length	Shoe size _______
Heel flap length	
Total foot length	

Decrease to _____ sts for toes _______ sts each side

Weight of sock	One sock ____ g/oz Two socks ___ g/oz
Amount of yarn used	Started with ____ g/oz Finished with ____ g/oz
Additional notes	
Date started	
Date finished	
Not finished? ☐	Why not?

Sock name

Made for ______________________________

Pattern

☐ cuff down ☐ toe up

Yarn

Needles

Cast on number	____ sts
Additional stitches	____ ankle ____calf ____foot ☐ none
No of rounds	____ cuff ____leg ____foot
Type of heel	☐ heel flap ☐ other ______________
Heel flap	______sts ______ rows No of V sts ____
Type of toe	
Leg length	
Foot length	Shoe size _______
Heel flap length	
Total foot length	

Decrease to _____ sts for toes ______ sts each side

Weight of sock	One sock ____ g/oz Two socks ____ g/oz
Amount of yarn used	Started with ____ g/oz Finished with ____ g/oz
Additional notes	
Date started	
Date finished	
Not finished? ☐	Why not?

Sock name 

Made for ______________________________

Pattern

☐ cuff down ☐ toe up

Yarn

Needles

Cast on number	____ sts
Additional stitches	____ ankle ____calf ____foot ☐ none
No of rounds	____ cuff ____leg ____foot
Type of heel	☐ heel flap ☐ other ________________
Heel flap	______sts ______ rows No of V sts ____
Type of toe	
Leg length	
Foot length	Shoe size _______
Heel flap length	
Total foot length	

Decrease to _____ sts for toes ______ sts each side

Weight of sock	One sock ____ g/oz Two socks ___ g/oz
Amount of yarn used	Started with ____ g/oz Finished with ____ g/oz
Additional notes	
Date started	
Date finished	
Not finished? ☐	Why not?

Sock name

Made for ______________________________

Pattern

☐ cuff down ☐ toe up

Yarn

Needles

Cast on number	____ sts
Additional stitches	____ ankle ____calf ____foot ☐ none
No of rounds	____ cuff ____leg ____foot
Type of heel	☐ heel flap ☐ other _____________
Heel flap	______sts ______ rows No of V sts ____
Type of toe	
Leg length	
Foot length	Shoe size _______
Heel flap length	
Total foot length	

Decrease to _____ sts for toes ______ sts each side

Weight of sock	One sock ____ g/oz Two socks ___ g/oz
Amount of yarn used	Started with ____ g/oz Finished with ____ g/oz
Additional notes	
Date started	
Date finished	
Not finished? ☐	Why not?

Sock name	38
Made for ______________________________	
Pattern ☐ cuff down ☐ toe up	
Yarn	
Needles	
Cast on number	____ sts
Additional stitches	____ ankle ____calf ____foot ☐ none
No of rounds	____ cuff ____leg ____foot
Type of heel	☐ heel flap ☐ other ______________
Heel flap	______sts ______ rows No of V sts ____
Type of toe	
Leg length	
Foot length	Shoe size _______
Heel flap length	
Total foot length	
Decrease to _____ sts for toes ______ sts each side	

Weight of sock	One sock ____ g/oz Two socks ___ g/oz
Amount of yarn used	Started with ____ g/oz Finished with ____ g/oz

Additional notes

Date started	
Date finished	
Not finished? ☐	Why not?

Sock name

Made for ______________________________

Pattern

☐ cuff down ☐ toe up

Yarn

Needles

Cast on number	____ sts
Additional stitches	____ ankle ____calf ____foot ☐ none
No of rounds	____ cuff ____leg ____foot
Type of heel	☐ heel flap ☐ other _____________
Heel flap	______sts ______ rows No of V sts ____
Type of toe	
Leg length	
Foot length	Shoe size _______
Heel flap length	
Total foot length	

Decrease to _____ sts for toes ______ sts each side

Weight of sock	One sock ____ g/oz Two socks ___ g/oz
Amount of yarn used	Started with ____ g/oz Finished with ____ g/oz
Additional notes	
Date started	
Date finished	
Not finished? ☐	Why not?

Sock name

40

Made for ______________________________

Pattern

☐ cuff down ☐ toe up

Yarn

Needles

Cast on number	____ sts
Additional stitches	____ ankle ____calf ____foot ☐ none
No of rounds	____ cuff ____leg ____foot
Type of heel	☐ heel flap ☐ other ______________
Heel flap	______sts ______ rows No of V sts ____
Type of toe	
Leg length	
Foot length	Shoe size _______
Heel flap length	
Total foot length	

Decrease to _____ sts for toes ______ sts each side

Weight of sock	One sock ____ g/oz Two socks ___ g/oz
Amount of yarn used	Started with ____ g/oz Finished with ____ g/oz
Additional notes	
Date started	
Date finished	
Not finished? ☐	Why not?

Sock name

Made for ______________________________

Pattern

☐ cuff down ☐ toe up

Yarn

Needles

Cast on number	____ sts
Additional stitches	____ ankle ____calf ____foot ☐ none
No of rounds	____ cuff ____leg ____foot
Type of heel	☐ heel flap ☐ other ______________
Heel flap	______sts ______ rows No of V sts ____
Type of toe	
Leg length	
Foot length	Shoe size _______
Heel flap length	
Total foot length	

Decrease to _____ sts for toes ______ sts each side

Weight of sock	One sock ____ g/oz Two socks ___ g/oz
Amount of yarn used	Started with ____ g/oz Finished with ____ g/oz

Additional notes

Date started	
Date finished	

Not finished? ☐ Why not?

Sock name

Made for ______________________________

Pattern

☐ cuff down ☐ toe up

Yarn

Needles

Cast on number	____ sts
Additional stitches	____ ankle ____calf ____foot ☐ none
No of rounds	____ cuff ____leg ____foot
Type of heel	☐ heel flap ☐ other ______________
Heel flap	______sts ______ rows No of V sts ____
Type of toe	
Leg length	
Foot length	Shoe size ______
Heel flap length	
Total foot length	

Decrease to _____ sts for toes ______ sts each side

Weight of sock	One sock ____ g/oz Two socks ___ g/oz
Amount of yarn used	Started with ____ g/oz Finished with ____ g/oz
Additional notes	
Date started	
Date finished	
Not finished? ☐	Why not?

Sock name 43 

Made for ______________________________

Pattern

☐ cuff down ☐ toe up

Yarn

Needles

Cast on number	____ sts
Additional stitches	____ ankle ____calf ____foot ☐ none
No of rounds	____ cuff ____leg ____foot
Type of heel	☐ heel flap ☐ other ______________
Heel flap	______sts ______ rows No of V sts ____
Type of toe	
Leg length	
Foot length	Shoe size _______
Heel flap length	
Total foot length	

Decrease to _____ sts for toes ______ sts each side

Weight of sock	One sock ____ g/oz Two socks ___ g/oz
Amount of yarn used	Started with ____ g/oz Finished with ____ g/oz
Additional notes	
Date started	
Date finished	
Not finished? ☐	Why not?

Sock name

Made for ______________________________

Pattern

☐ cuff down ☐ toe up

Yarn

Needles

Cast on number	____ sts
Additional stitches	____ ankle ____calf ____foot ☐ none
No of rounds	____ cuff ____leg ____foot
Type of heel	☐ heel flap ☐ other ______________
Heel flap	______sts ______ rows No of V sts ____
Type of toe	
Leg length	
Foot length	Shoe size ______
Heel flap length	
Total foot length	

Decrease to _____ sts for toes ______ sts each side

Weight of sock	One sock ____ g/oz Two socks ___ g/oz
Amount of yarn used	Started with ____ g/oz Finished with ____ g/oz
Additional notes	
Date started	
Date finished	
Not finished? ☐	Why not?

Sock name 

Made for ______________________________

Pattern

☐ cuff down ☐ toe up

Yarn

Needles

Cast on number	____ sts
Additional stitches	____ ankle ____calf ____foot ☐ none
No of rounds	____ cuff ____leg ____foot
Type of heel	☐ heel flap ☐ other ________________
Heel flap	______sts ______ rows No of V sts ____
Type of toe	
Leg length	
Foot length	Shoe size _______
Heel flap length	
Total foot length	

Decrease to _____ sts for toes _______ sts each side

Weight of sock	One sock ____ g/oz Two socks ___ g/oz
Amount of yarn used	Started with ____ g/oz Finished with ____ g/oz
Additional notes	
Date started	
Date finished	
Not finished? ☐	Why not?

Sock name 46

Made for ______________________________

Pattern

☐ cuff down ☐ toe up

Yarn

Needles

Cast on number	____ sts
Additional stitches	____ ankle ____calf ____foot ☐ none
No of rounds	____ cuff ____leg ____foot
Type of heel	☐ heel flap ☐ other ______________
Heel flap	______sts ______ rows No of V sts ____
Type of toe	
Leg length	
Foot length	Shoe size _______
Heel flap length	
Total foot length	

Decrease to _____ sts for toes ______ sts each side

Weight of sock	One sock ____ g/oz Two socks ___ g/oz
Amount of yarn used	Started with ____ g/oz Finished with ____ g/oz
Additional notes	
Date started	
Date finished	
Not finished? ☐	Why not?

Sock name

Made for ______________________________

Pattern

☐ cuff down ☐ toe up

Yarn

Needles

Cast on number	____ sts
Additional stitches	____ ankle ____calf ____foot ☐ none
No of rounds	____ cuff ____leg ____foot
Type of heel	☐ heel flap ☐ other ______________
Heel flap	_____sts _____ rows No of V sts ____
Type of toe	
Leg length	
Foot length	Shoe size ______
Heel flap length	
Total foot length	

Decrease to _____ sts for toes _______ sts each side

Weight of sock	One sock ____ g/oz Two socks ___ g/oz
Amount of yarn used	Started with ____ g/oz Finished with ____ g/oz
Additional notes	
Date started	
Date finished	
Not finished? ☐	Why not?

Sock name

48 

Made for ________________________________

Pattern

☐ cuff down ☐ toe up

Yarn

Needles

Cast on number	____ sts
Additional stitches	____ ankle ____calf ____foot ☐ none
No of rounds	____ cuff ____leg ____foot
Type of heel	☐ heel flap ☐ other ________________
Heel flap	______sts ______ rows No of V sts ____
Type of toe	
Leg length	
Foot length	Shoe size _______
Heel flap length	
Total foot length	

Decrease to _____ sts for toes _______ sts each side

Weight of sock	One sock ____ g/oz Two socks ___ g/oz
Amount of yarn used	Started with ____ g/oz Finished with ____ g/oz
Additional notes	
Date started	
Date finished	
Not finished? ☐	Why not?

Sock name

49

Made for ______________________________

Pattern

☐ cuff down ☐ toe up

Yarn

Needles

Cast on number	____ sts
Additional stitches	____ ankle ____calf ____foot ☐ none
No of rounds	____ cuff ____leg ____foot
Type of heel	☐ heel flap ☐ other ______________
Heel flap	______sts ______ rows No of V sts ____
Type of toe	
Leg length	
Foot length	Shoe size _______
Heel flap length	
Total foot length	

Decrease to _____ sts for toes _______ sts each side

<table>
<tr><td>Weight of sock</td><td>One sock ____ g/oz   Two socks ___ g/oz</td></tr>
<tr><td>Amount of yarn used</td><td>Started with ____ g/oz
Finished with ____ g/oz</td></tr>
<tr><td colspan="2">Additional notes</td></tr>
<tr><td>Date started</td><td></td></tr>
<tr><td>Date finished</td><td></td></tr>
<tr><td>Not finished? ☐</td><td>Why not?</td></tr>
</table>

Sock name

50

Made for ______________________________

Pattern

☐ cuff down ☐ toe up

Yarn

Needles

Cast on number	____ sts
Additional stitches	____ ankle ____calf ____foot ☐ none
No of rounds	____ cuff ____leg ____foot
Type of heel	☐ heel flap ☐ other ______________
Heel flap	______sts ______ rows No of V sts ____
Type of toe	
Leg length	
Foot length	Shoe size ______
Heel flap length	
Total foot length	

Decrease to _____ sts for toes ______ sts each side

Weight of sock	One sock ____ g/oz Two socks ___ g/oz
Amount of yarn used	Started with ____ g/oz Finished with ____ g/oz
Additional notes	
Date started	
Date finished	
Not finished? ☐	Why not?

Project Super Socks - Master Plan

Every sock superstar needs a book of blueprints!

This book isn't written the wrong way round – I've created it this way so that the most important information on the socks that you have knitted or are knitting at the moment is right at the front where you need it.

Coming up is the **Sock Stitch Calculation** from the Winwick Mum Sockalong, the **Basic 4ply Socks pattern** and the **Basic 8ply (DK) Socks pattern** so that you've always got a sock pattern to hand – and a quick **Kitchener Stitch** reminder! There's also a handy page of links to the Winwick Mum Sockalong and other patterns.

Page

Links

For sock knitting beginners, the Winwick Mum Sockalong step-by-step tutorials are perfect for getting you started on your sock journey!

www.winwickmum.co.uk/sockalong

For more patterns and next-step tutorials, have a look at the Patterns and Printables page:

www.winwickmum.co.uk/patterns-and-printables

If you're a fan of self-striping yarn, don't miss the Winwick Mum Collections of West Yorkshire Spinners Signature 4ply!

www.winwickmum.co.uk/winwick-mum-yarn

Find me on social media!

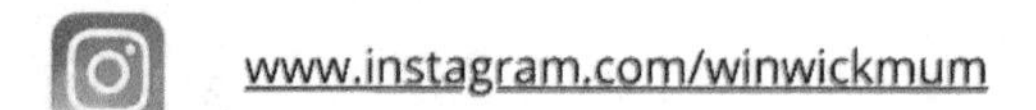

www.pinterest.com/winwickmum

www.ravelry.com/designers/winwick-mum

www.payhip.com/winwickmum

Winwick
MUM

Sock Stitch Calculation

If you search the internet, there are plenty of methods for working out the number of stitches you will need, some of them based on foot width and others on calf or ankle size. A good method, which can be adapted to any sock yarn, is this one which takes into account the size of your feet and the tension that you knit to.

The number of stitches that you choose to cast on **must always be divisible by 4**, so choose the nearest multiple of 4 to the result that you get from your stitch calculation.

Measure around the ball of your foot (in inches) and multiply that measurement by the number of stitches per inch from your swatch – always make sure that you swatch in the round to match the way you're going to knit your sock.

Here's an example:

8 (foot measurement) x 8 (stitches per inch) = 64

Next, you need to allow for the negative ease (stretch in the knitted fabric) so take 10% off the total – in my case, 10% of 64 stitches would be 6.4 but it's easiest to round it up or down to the nearest whole number. This would make the new calculation

64 (original number of stitches) – 6 (10% negative ease) = 58

Remember that the number of stitches that you cast on needs to be a multiple of 4, so you could cast on either 56 or 60 stitches. It's generally better for your sock fabric to be tighter than, say, for a jumper as that makes it more hard-wearing, but you don't want it so tight that it pulls across your foot.

In the end, the gauge becomes a matter of preference – some people like tighter socks, others prefer looser socks and as you complete more pairs, you will see which you prefer for yourself. The nice thing about hand-knits is that you can try your socks on at every stage to make sure they are going to fit perfectly.

If you want to, you can take other measurements – say, ankle and calf – if you want to knit for somebody who might need a wider leg to the sock. Work out the stitch count for each of these measurements and then cast on and adjust accordingly. There is no rule with hand knit socks that says the sock has to be the same stitch count throughout!

You can use this calculation for any weight of yarn and the pattern and tutorials will also work with any type of yarn, so there is no limit to the socks you can make!

SOCK STITCH CALCULATION

Circumference of foot in inches

X

Number of stitches per inch

—

10% for negative ease (stretch)

You can find the online tutorial for this section here:
https://www.winwickmum.co.uk/sockalong

and a video to help here:
https://www.winwickmum.co.uk/winwick-mum-sockalong-help

If you've got a copy of *Super Socks,* you'll find it on page 20.

Basic 4ply Socks by Winwick Mum

Whether to fill up your own sock drawer or to give to knit-worthy friends and loved ones, hand knitted socks are the very best kind of socks! The Basic 4ply Socks are constructed as top down socks with a heel flap and gusset. The heel is knitted in heel stitch which creates a durable, cushioned heel.

This pattern can be used on its own or in conjunction with the **Winwick Mum Sockalong** beginner sock knitting tutorials which are available online for free here: **www.winwickmum.co.uk/sockalong**

Size	To fit ball of foot circumference 8in; 20cm, and advice is given to adjust the size for any foot
Tension	30 stitches to 4in; 10cm in stocking stitch (worked in the round) on 2.5mm needles (or size required for tension)
Yarn	1 x 100g (or 2 x 50g) 4ply yarn. Yarn pictured is Regia Design Line 4ply - Kaffe Fassett, (shade now discontinued)

Materials

2.5mm needles – short circular needle, DPNs (double pointed needles) or 80 cm circular for magic loop
1 set DPNs size 3.0mm (optional for a looser cuff)
1 set DPNs size 2.5mm (not required for magic loop)
Stitch holder (optional)
Stitch markers
Wool needle

Abbreviations

K	Knit
K2tog	Knit two stitches together
P	Purl
Sl1	Slip 1 stitch purlwise holding yarn to the back of your work
SSK	Slip the first stitch on the left hand needle knitwise onto the right hand needle, slip the second stitch on the left hand needle purlwise onto the right hand needle, slip both stitches back onto the left hand needle and knit together through back loop
St(s)	Stitch(es)
( )	Repeat instructions inside brackets

How to adjust the size for this pattern

There is only one size given for this pattern, but you can use this as a guide for any other size. Hand knitted socks are measured by width and not length, which is easily adjusted, so to get the perfect fit for the person you are knitting for, it is best to measure their feet first and use the **Sock Stitch Calculation** to find out the right number to cast on. It's very easy to do, and once you have the numbers, you can use them for any pair of socks in the same weight of yarn. The Sock Stitch Calculation, along with a tension tutorial and a video to help can be found here: **https://bit.ly/sockstitchcalculation**

Pattern notes

It is often easier to cast on using DPNs before changing to the short circular needle. If you want to use magic loop you will be able to cast on with the larger circular needle if you prefer to do so, but remember not to pull your cast on stitches too tight. If you use DPNs, you might find it easiest to cast on and work 2 rows before dividing the stitches across the needles.

I have given an indication of the number of rows or rounds that I knit for my socks, but do remember that these are just a guide to give you some idea of how long you should be knitting for! It's always best to check the measurements against your own feet, or those of the person you are knitting for.

Pattern

Cast on 60 stitches using 3.0mm needle. The pattern has been written for a cast on with straight needles which makes it easier for you to join into the round without twisting the stitches.

Row 1: (K2, P2), repeat to end, turn.
Row 2: (K2, P2), repeat to end, turn.

Change to 2.5mm needles. At this point, change to a short circular needle, magic loop or divide the stitches across DPNs and join into a circle, **place marker**. You will sew up the small gap where you knitted the first two rows later.

Continue in K2, P2 rib for 14 more rounds or until desired length of rib (I knit 16 rounds of rib).

Continue to knit each round until desired length before start of heel (for me, this is 72 rounds in total including the rib).

Heel Flap

Change to 2.5mm DPNs if you are using a short circular needle. You are going to create the heel flap from half the number of stitches that you cast on, so if you have cast on more or less than 60 stitches, remember to adjust the number of stitches when you start the heel flap. Knitting the first two stitches of row 1 will help to stop a hole forming at the gusset.

Row 1: K2, (Sl1, K1) until you have 30 sts on your needle, turn.
Row 2: Sl1, P to end, turn.
Row 3: (Sl1, K1) to end, turn.

Repeat rows 2 and 3 until heel measures approximately 2in; 5cm, finishing on row 3 (for me, this is approximately 35 rows). If you want to make the heel flap longer, continue knitting rows 2 and 3 until you reach the desired length, but remember that you will need to pick up more stitches to create the gusset. You can check that the heel flap is long enough by measuring it against your foot from your ankle bone to the floor.

<u>Turn heel</u>

For a larger or smaller sock, you will need to alter the number of purl stitches in the first row of the heel (marked in bold below), increasing by 1 stitch for each block of 4 stitches extra that you cast on, or decreasing by 1 st for each block of 4 sts less than 60 sts. For example, if you cast on 64 stitches, your first row would be Sl1, P17, P2tog, P1, turn

Row 1: Sl1, **P16**, P2tog, P1, turn.
Row 2: Sl1, K5, SSK, K1, turn.
Row 3: Sl1, P6, P2tog, P1, turn.
Row 4: Sl1, K7, SSK, K1, turn.

Continue in this way, adding one stitch between slip stitch and SSK or P2tog on each row (ie, **Row 5**: Sl1, **P8**, P2tog, P1; **Row 6**: Sl1, **K9**, SSK, K1, etc) until all of the heel stitches are used. Depending on how many stitches are in your heel flap, you may find that the K1 and P1 stitch is not required at the end of the last two rows.

Knit across heel stitches if required to bring you to the left hand side of the heel ready to pick up 1 st for every 2 rows of heel flap knitted. Remember that if you made the heel flap bigger, you will need to pick up more stitches. Once you have picked up the stitches, **place marker** to indicate new beginning of round. Knit across the top of the foot, **place marker**, then pick up 1 st for every 2 rows knitted up the other side of the heel. Knit across the top of the heel and then shape gusset as follows.

Note: If you are using DPNs and/or have placed your stitches on a stitch holder, you can arrange the needles as follows: Needle 1 for stitches across heel, Needle 2 for picked-up stitches down side of foot, Needle 3 for stitches across top of foot (knit stitches off stitch holder if required), Needle 4 for picked-up stitches on other side of foot. You may find that stitch markers are not required at first.

Shape gusset

Round 1: K to 3 sts before the marker, K2tog, K1, **slip marker**, knit to next marker, **slip marker**, K1, SSK, K to marker.

Round 2: **Slip marker**, knit to next marker, **slip marker**, knit to 3 sts before marker.

Round 3: K2tog, K1, **slip marker**, knit to next marker, **slip marker**, K1 SSK, K to marker.

Repeat rounds 2 and 3 to shape the gusset. Continue in this way, decreasing by two stitches at the gusset on every other round until there are 60 sts on the needle. If you want to remove the marker at the SSK decrease you can do that now, but keep the other one in to indicate the start of your round.

Once you have 60 stitches again, continue to knit each round until you reach approximately 2in; 5cm before the desired length ready to start the toes. For my UK size 5 feet, this is about 48 rounds. Don't be afraid to try your sock on before decreasing for the toes!

Toes

At some point whilst decreasing for the toes, if you are using a short circular needle you may need to change back to DPNs as the number of stitches becomes too small for the circular. It's up to you when you choose to do that, and how you distribute the stitches across the needles; just keep following the pattern as set below. Create the toes as follows:

Round 1: K1, SSK, K24 sts, K2tog, K1, **place marker** (if required), K1, SSK, K24 sts, K2tog, K1. (56 sts)
Round 2: Knit one round, **slipping markers** as you come to them.
Round 3: K1, SSK, K to 3 sts before marker, K2tog, K1, **slip marker**, K1, SSK, K to 3 sts before marker, K2tog, K1. (52 sts)

Repeat rounds 2 and 3 until you have 28 stitches left and divide these between two needles so that front and back of socks match.

Graft toes using Kitchener stitch, weave in all ends and sew up the small gap at the cuff where you cast on.

Basic 8ply (DK) Socks by Winwick Mum

Whether to fill up your own sock drawer or to give to knit-worthy friends and loved ones, hand knitted socks are the very best kind of socks!

The Basic 8ply (DK) Socks are constructed as top down socks with a heel flap and gusset. The heel is knitted in heel stitch which creates a durable, cushioned heel.

This pattern can be used on its own or in conjunction with the **Winwick Mum Sockalong** beginner sock knitting tutorials which are available online for free here: **www.winwickmum.co.uk/sockalong**

Size To fit ball of foot circumference 8in; 20cm, and advice is given to adjust the size for any foot

Tension 22 stitches to 4in; 10cm in stocking stitch (worked in the round) on 3.5mm needles (or size required for tension)

Yarn 1 x 150g 8ply yarn. Yarn pictured is Regia Iglu Color in shade 8991 Lappland (now discontinued)

*** Many DK yarns are sold in 100g balls and one ball should be enough for a pair of socks, obviously depending on the size of the foot!*

Materials

3.5mm needles – short circular needle, DPNs (double pointed needles) or 80 cm circular for magic loop
1 set DPNs size 4.0mm (optional for a looser cuff)
1 set DPNs size 3.5mm (not required for magic loop)

Stitch holder (optional)
Stitch markers
Wool needle

Abbreviations

K	Knit
K2tog	Knit two stitches together
P	Purl
Sl1	Slip 1 stitch purlwise holding yarn to the back of your work
SSK	Slip the first stitch on the left hand needle knitwise onto the right hand needle, slip the second stitch on the left hand needle purlwise onto the right hand needle, slip both stitches back onto the left hand needle and knit together through back loop
Sts	Stitch(es)
( )	Repeat instructions inside brackets

How to adjust the size for this pattern

There is only one size given for this pattern, but you can use this as a guide for any other size. Hand knitted socks are measured by width and not length, which is easily adjusted, so to get the perfect fit for the person you are knitting for, it is best to measure their feet first and use the **Sock Stitch Calculation** to find out the right number to cast on. It's very easy to do, and once you have the numbers, you can use them for any pair of socks in the same weight of yarn. The Sock Stitch Calculation, along with a tension tutorial and a video to help can be found here: **https://bit.ly/sockstitchcalculation**

Pattern notes

It is often easier to cast on using DPNs before changing to the short circular needle. If you want to use magic loop you will be able to cast on with the larger circular needle if you prefer to do so, but remember not to pull your cast on stitches too tight. If you use DPNs, you might find it easiest to cast on and work 2 rows before dividing the stitches across the needles.

I have given an indication of the number of rows or rounds that I knit for my socks, but do remember that these are just a guide to give you some idea of how long you should be knitting for! It's always best to check the measurements against your own feet, or those of the person you are knitting for.

Pattern

Cast on 44 stitches using 4.0mm needle. The pattern has been written for a cast on with straight needles which makes it easier for you to join into the round without twisting the stitches.

Row 1: (K2, P2), repeat to end, turn.
Row 2: (K2, P2), repeat to end, turn.

Change to 3.5mm needles. At this point, change to a short circular needle, magic loop or divide the stitches across DPNs and join into a circle, **place marker**. You will sew up the small gap where you knitted the first two rows later.

Continue in K2, P2 rib for 8 more rounds or until desired length of rib (I knit 10 rounds of rib).

Continue to knit each round until desired length before start of heel (for me, this is 48 rounds in total including the rib).

Heel Flap

Change to 3.5mm DPNs if you are using a small circular. You are going to create the heel flap from half the number of stitches that you cast on, so if you have cast on more or less than 44 stitches, remember to adjust the number of stitches when you start the heel flap. Knitting the first two stitches of row 1 will help to stop a hole forming at the gusset.

Row 1: K2, (Sl1, K1) until you have 22 sts on your needle, turn.
Row 2: Sl1, P to end, turn.
Row 3: (Sl1, K1) to end, turn.

Repeat rows 2 and 3 until heel measures approximately 2in; 5cm, finishing on row 3 (for me, this is approximately 19 rows). If you want to make the heel flap longer, continue knitting rows 2 and 3 until you reach the desired length, but remember that you will need to pick up more stitches to create the gusset. You can check that the heel flap is long enough by measuring it against your foot from your ankle bone to the floor.

Turn heel

For a larger or smaller sock, you will need to alter the number of purl stitches in the first row of the heel (marked in bold below), increasing by 1 stitch for each block of 4 stitches extra that you cast on, or decreasing by 1 stitch for each block of 4 stitches less than 44 stitches. For example, if you cast on 48 stitches, your first row would be Sl1, P13, P2tog, P1, turn

Row 1: Sl1, **P12**, P2tog, P1, turn.
Row 2: Sl1, K5, SSK, K1, turn.
Row 3: Sl1, P6, P2tog, P1, turn.
Row 4: Sl1, K7, SSK, K1, turn.

Continue in this way, adding one stitch between slip stitch and SSK or P2tog on each row (ie, **Row 5**: Sl1, **P8**, P2tog, P1; **Row 6**: Sl1, **K9**, SSK, K1, etc) until all of the heel stitches are used. Depending on how many stitches are in your heel flap, you may find that the K1 and P1 stitch is not required at the end of the last two rows. Knit across heel stitches if required to bring you to the left hand side of the heel ready to pick up 1 st for every 2 rows of heel flap knitted. Remember that if you made the heel flap bigger, you will need to pick up more stitches. Once you have picked up the stitches, **place marker** to indicate new beginning of round. Knit across the top of the foot, **place marker**, then pick up 1 st for every 2 rows knitted up the other side of the heel. Knit across the top of the heel and then shape gusset as follows.

Note: If you are using DPNs and/or have placed your stitches on a stitch holder, you can arrange the needles as follows: Needle 1 for stitches across heel, Needle 2 for picked-up stitches down side of foot, Needle 3 for stitches across top of foot (knit stitches off stitch holder if required), Needle 4 for picked-up stitches on other side of foot. You may find that stitch markers are not required at first.

Shape gusset

Round 1: K to 3 sts before the marker, K2tog, K1, **slip marker**, knit to next marker, **slip marker**, K1, SSK, K to marker.
Round 2: **Slip marker**, knit to next marker, **slip marker**, knit to 3 sts before marker.
Round 3: K2tog, K1, **slip marker**, knit to next marker, **slip marker**, K1, SSK, K to marker.

Repeat rounds 2 and 3 to shape the gusset. Continue in this way, decreasing by two stitches at the gusset on every other row until there are 44 stitches on the needle. If you want to remove the marker at the SSK decrease you can do that now, but keep the other one in to indicate the start of your round.

Once you have 44 stitches again, continue to knit each round until you reach approximately 1.2 in;3cm before the desired length ready to start the toes. For my UK size 5 feet, this is about 42 rounds. Don't be afraid to try your sock on before decreasing for the toes!

Toes

At some point whilst decreasing for the toes, if you are using a short circular needle you may need to change back to DPNs as the number of stitches becomes too small for the circular.

It's up to you when you choose to do that, and how you distribute the stitches across the needles; just keep following the pattern as set below. Create the toes as follows:

Round 1: K1, SSK, K16 sts, K2tog, K1, **place marker** (if required), K1, SSK, K16 sts, K2tog, K1. (40sts)
Round 2: Knit one round, **slipping markers** as you come to them.
Round 3: K1, SSK, K to 3 sts before marker, K2tog, K1, **slip marker**, K1, SSK, K to 3 sts before marker, K2tog, K1. (36sts)

Repeat rounds 2 and 3 until you have 28 stitches left and divide these between two needles so that front and back of socks match.

Graft toes using Kitchener stitch, weave in all ends and sew up the small gap at the cuff where you cast on.

Winwick Mum books

Not everybody can or wants to be online all the time so as well as the free online tutorials, you can find Winwick Mum tutorials in these paperback and eBooks as well.

Super Socks contains the Winwick Mum Sockalong tutorials – all of the same information as you'll find on the blog but with the sock instructions set out by needle type, rather than sock section.

The Basic 4ply Socks pattern is included, along with the Basic 6ply Socks pattern.

More Super Socks was written as a next-step guide to adding patterns to your basic socks. You'll find four photo/video tutorials for creating cables, lace, colourwork and intarsia which are also available on the blog.

There are also four exclusive patterns building on the skills that you've learnt through the book to help you feel more confident about tackling other patterns.

Both books are available from Amazon, the Winwick Mum blog, Wool Warehouse, Black Sheep Wools and other yarn shops, and by request from your local bookstore.

About Winwick Mum

Christine Perry is an award-winning blogger and "sock knitting enabler" and has taught thousands of beginners to knit socks through her free online Sockalong tutorials. She passionately believes that the world always needs more sock knitters and would be very happy to knit socks all day except for the disappointing discovery that housework won't do itself and her family can't live on fresh air. Luckily, they all appreciate hand-knitted socks so feeding them is no hardship ☺

You can read more about Christine and the Winwick Mum blog at **www.winwickmum.co.uk/about-me**

If you'd like to join the mailing list to get regular blog updates and a FREE Kitchener Stitch guide to download, you can do that through this link:

www.winwickmum.co.uk/mailing-list

This notebook is dedicated to everyone who knows that the world is a better place for having hand knit socks – and sock knitters – in it!

Kitchener Stitch instructions

There are several ways to finish off the toes of your socks, but my favourite is the Kitchener Stitch which gives a lovely seam-free toe.

I've put these instructions right at the very back of this book so that they'll be easy to find when you need them – and don't forget that it's best to work the Kitchener Stitch when you're not likely to be disturbed!

You can find step-by-step photo instructions for working the Kitchener stitch at **www.winwickmum.co.uk/sockalong**

Leave a tail end length of approx. 12in; 30cm from your sock, cut yarn and thread onto a wool needle. Insert the wool needle into the stitches as follows:

Set up stitches (optional)

1 Front needle: **1st** st purlwise, leave on
2 Back needle: **1st** st knitwise, leave on

Rest of stitches

3 Front needle: **1st** st knitwise, take off
4 Front needle: **2nd** st purlwise, leave on
5 Back needle: **1st** st purlwise, take off
6 Back needle: **2nd** st knitwise, leave on

Repeat steps 3 to 6, taking the yarn through the last two sts just once before fastening off – this will help avoid an "ear".

Made in the USA
Las Vegas, NV
12 April 2024